# ACKNOWLEDGEMENTS

The publishers would like to thank the following sources for permission to reproduce illustrations:

BRIDGEMAN ART LIBRARY: pp.29, 62B; E.T.ARCHIVE: pp.28, 83; MARY EVANS PICTURE LIBRARY: pp.14, 80; FINE ART PHOTOGRAPHIC LIBRARY: pp.6–7, 8, 11, 17, 18, 20, 22, 25, 26, 31, 34, 36, 39, 40, 41, 43, 44, 46, 49, 51, 52, 55T, 58, 60, 63, 65, 68, 71, 72, 75, 77, 78, 81, 85, 86, 89, 92, 94, 98, 99, 101, 102, 105, 109

The publishers would also like to acknowledge the following writers and poets: ANDERS, ISABEL, *Walking with the Shepherd* (Nelson, 1994). BARNES, EMILIE, *Survival for Busy Women* (Harvest House, 1993). BENSON, PEGGY, *Listening for a God Who Whispers* (Nelson, 1991). BETHUNE, MARY MCLEOD, "My Last Will and Testament." BOONE, SHIRLEY, *One Woman's Liberation* (Nelson, 1972). BRADSTREET, ANNE, *Meditations Divine and Moral,* 1664. BRONTË, EMILY, "No Coward Soul Is Mine," *The Complete Poems of Emily Jane Brontë* (Columbia University Press, 1941). BROWNING, ELIZABETH BARRETT, "De Profundis," *The Complete Poetry of Miss Browning*, edited by H. E. Scudder (Houghton Mifflin, 1900). BUCK, PEARL S., *To My Daughters with Love* (Buccaneer Books, 1992). BUSH, BARBARA, *A Memoir*, Lisa Drew Books (Charles Scribner's Sons, 1994). CANNON, SARAH (MINNIE PEARL), *An Autobiography* (Simon & Schuster, 1980). CARNEY, JULIA A. FLETCHER, "Little Things," *The Best-Loved Poems of the American People*, Hazel Felleman (Doubleday, 1936). CASWELL, HELEN, *A Little Book of Friendship* (Nelson, 1995). CATHER, WILLA, *O Pioneers!* (Dover, 1993). CLAIRMONT, PATSY, *Under His Wings* (Focus on the Family, 1994). DAME JULIAN OF NORWICH, *Revelations of Divine Love*. Translation in *A Book of Comfort* by ELIZABETH GOUDGE (Coward-McCann, 1964). DARGATZ, JAN, *Women & Power* (Nelson, 1995). DICKINSON, EMILY, *The Complete Poems of Emily Dickinson* (Buccaneer Books, 1990). EARHART, AMELIA, "Courage," *The Sound of Wings: The Life of Amelia Earhart*, Mary S. Lovell (St. Martin, 1991). ELLIOT, ELISABETH, *The Path of Loneliness* (Nelson, 1988). EZELL, LEE, *The Cinderella Syndrome* (Vine Books, 1985). FERNANDEZ, MARY JOE, *True Champions: The Good Guys in American Sports Speak Out*, compiled by Mike Toule (Summit Group, 1994). FRANK, ANNE, *Diary of a Young Girl* (Knopf, 1994). GRAHAM, RUTH BELL, *Legacy of a Pack Rat* (Nelson, 1989). GRANT, AMY, in *Sound Expressions* by John J. Thompson (Chariot Family Publishers). GRIFFIN, EMILIE, *Homeward Voyager: Reflections on Life-Changes* (Servant Publications, 1994). HASKINS, MINNIE LOUISE, "Introduction," *The Desert* (Minnie L. Haskins, 1920). HIGGS, LIZ CURTIS, *Does Dinner in a Bucket Count?* (Nelson, 1993). HILDEGARD OF BINGEN, *Meditations with Hildegard of Bingen*, translated by Gabrielle Uhlein, Santa Fe, N.M. (Bear and Company, 1982). HURNARD, HANNAH, *Kingdom of Love* (Tyndale, 1978). JAMES, KAY COLES, *Never Forget* (Zondervan, 1993). JENSEN, MARGARET, *The Sun Is Shining on the Other Side* (Nelson, 1995).

JILLIAN, ANN, "Out of the Night," *Aspire*, December 1994/January 1995. JOHNSON, BARBARA, in "A Funny Woman Gets Serious" by Nancie Carmichael, *Virtue*, April 1995. JOHNSON, BARBARA, *Splashes of Joy in the Cesspools of Life* (Word, 1992). JOHNSON, CLAUDIA "Lady Bird," from *Women's Wisdom Through the Ages* (Harold Shaw, 1994). JOHNSON, VICTORIA, *Aspire*, April/May 1995. JOYNER, FLORENCE GRIFFITH, *The Olympics: A History of the Games* (Oxmoor House, 1993). JUDD, NAOMI, *Love Can Build a Bridge*, Fawcett Crest (Ballantine, 1993). KETTERMAN, GRACE, *Parenting the Difficult Child* (Nelson, 1994). LANE, DEFORIA, *Music as Medicine* (Zondervan, 1994). L'ENGLE, MADELEINE, *A Circle of Quiet* (HarperCollins, 1984). LITTAUER, FLORENCE, *How to Get Along with Difficult People* (Harvest House, 1984). LITTAUER, FLORENCE, *Silver Boxes* (Word, 1989). MARSHALL, CATHERINE, *Something More* (Avon, 1994). McCULLOUGH, MAMIE, *I Can, You Can Too!* (Nelson, 1987). MILLAY, EDNA ST. VINCENT, "God's World," *The Family Book of Best-Loved Poems*, David L. George (Doubleday, 1952). MOTHER TERESA, *A Gift from God* (Harper & Row, 1975). NEWENHUYSE, ELIZABETH CODY, "Spruce Up Your Self-Esteem," *Aspire*, August/September 1994. NORTHINGTON, JAN, *Separated and Waiting* (Nelson, 1994). PARKS, ROSA, *Quiet Strength* (Zondervan, 1995). PINE, BARBARA ROBERTS, *Life with a Capital "L"* (Nelson, 1994). PRICE, EUGENIA, *What Really Matters* (Jove Publications, 1985). RABEY, LOIS MOWDAY, *Coming of Age* (Nelson, 1995). RHODE, NAOMI, *The Gift of Family* (Nelson, 1991). ROGERS, DALE EVANS, *The Woman at the Well* (Bantam, 1976). ROOSEVELT, ELEANOR, *The Autobiography of Eleanor Roosevelt* (Da Capo, 1992). ROSSETTI, CHRISTINA, "Hope," *Complete Poems* (Lightyear, 1992). ST. TERESA OF AVILA, *Interior Castle* (Morehouse Publishing, 1991). SHAW, LUCI, in "Writing Her River" by Vicki Huffman, *A Better Tomorrow*, March/April 1995. SMITH, HANNAH WHITALL, *The Christian's Secret of a Happy Life* (Fleming H. Revell, 1992). TEN BOOM, CORRIE, *Clippings from My Notebook* (Nelson, 1982). TIRABASSI, BECKY, *Being a Wild, Wonderful Woman for God* (Zondervan, 1994). TUBMAN, HARRIET, *Scenes in the Life of Harriet Tubman* (Ayer, 1869). WELTY, EUDORA, *The Wide Net & Other Stories* (Harcourt Brace & Co., 1974). WESLEY, SUSANNA, from *A Guide to Prayer for Ministers and Other Servants*, Reuben Job & Norman Shawchuck (Upper Room Books, 1992). WHELCHEL, MARY, *How to Thrive from 9 to 5* (Word, 1995). WHITESTONE, HEATHER, in "Meet Miss America" by Amy Jennings Adams, *Parent Life*, March 1995. WILDER, LAURA INGALLS, from *Little House in the Ozarks*, edited by Stephen Hines (Nelson, 1991).

*Designed and produced by* THE BRIDGEWATER BOOK CO. LTD.

*Designed by* SARAH STANLEY

*Picture Research by* FELICITY COX

Published in Nashville, Tennessee, by Thomas Nelson, Inc., Publishers, and distributed in Canada by Word Communications, Ltd., Richmond, British Columbia.

CLB 4738

Unless otherwise noted, the Bible version used in this publication is THE NEW KING JAMES VERSION. Copyright © 1979, 1980, 1982, 1990, Thomas Nelson, Inc., Publishers.

The Scripture quotation noted CEV is from the Contemporary English Version. Copyright © 1991, American Bible Society.

ISBN 0–7852–7963–6

Printed in Singapore

1 2 3 4 5 6 — 01 00 99 98 97 96

TITLE PAGE: *Dreaming*, CHECA Y SANZ, ULPIANO (1860–1916)

A GIFT FOR

FROM

. . . . . . . . . . . . . . . . . . . . . . . . . . . . . . . . . . . . . . . . . . . .

. . . . . . . . . . . . . . . . . . . . . . . . . . . . . . . . . . . . . . . . . . . .

OLIVER
NELSON

**THOMAS NELSON PUBLISHERS**

# A Woman's Book of Days

INSPIRATION

AND

CELEBRATION

A
# Woman's

**JANUARY**

*Go out into the darkness and put
your hand into the Hand of God.
That shall be to you better than
light and safer than a known way.*
MINNIE LOUISE HASKINS

# JANUARY

1

2

3

4

5

6

7

NOTES

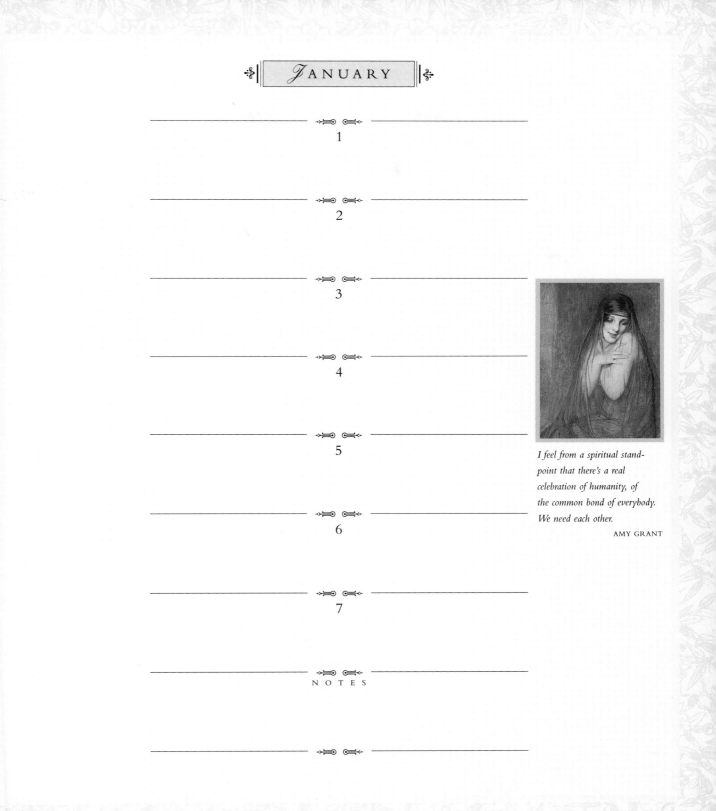

*I feel from a spiritual standpoint that there's a real celebration of humanity, of the common bond of everybody. We need each other.*

AMY GRANT

LEFT: *Confidences*, VITTORIO REGGIANINI (19TH CENTURY)

———————— ✦ ❦ ✦ ————————

8

———————— ✦ ❦ ✦ ————————

9

———————— ✦ ❦ ✦ ————————

10

———————— ✦ ❦ ✦ ————————

11

———————— ✦ ❦ ✦ ————————

12

———————— ✦ ❦ ✦ ————————

13

———————— ✦ ❦ ✦ ————————

14

———————— ✦ ❦ ✦ ————————

NOTES

———————— ✦ ❦ ✦ ————————

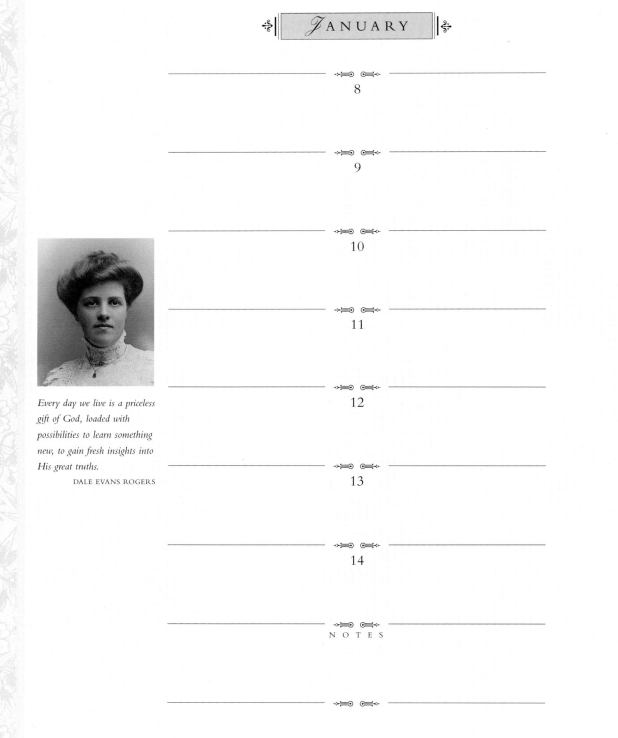

*Every day we live is a priceless gift of God, loaded with possibilities to learn something new, to gain fresh insights into His great truths.*

DALE EVANS ROGERS

*A Labour of Love*, WILLIAM M. HAY (fl. 1852–1881)

# JANUARY

---
15

---
16

---
17

---
18

---

"CRAYON"

## JANUARY

—— 19 ——

—— 20 ——

—— 21 ——

NOTES

*If God is here for us and not elsewhere,*
*then in fact this place is holy and*
*this moment is sacred.*

ISABEL ANDERS

*Florence Nightingale at Sartari*, ANONYMOUS (c. 1854)

## JANUARY

_____

22

_____

23

_____

24

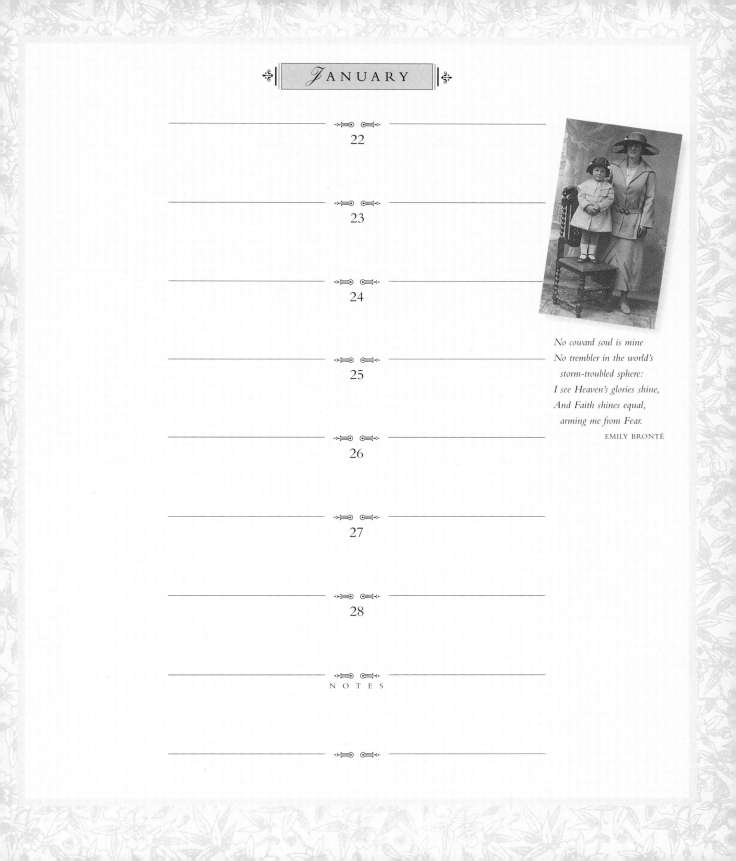

_____

25

*No coward soul is mine*
*No trembler in the world's*
*   storm-troubled sphere:*
*I see Heaven's glories shine,*
*And Faith shines equal,*
*   arming me from Fear.*

EMILY BRONTË

_____

26

_____

27

_____

28

_____

NOTES

_____

—⟫ ⟪—

29

—⟫ ⟪—

30

—⟫ ⟪—

31

—⟫ ⟪—

NOTES

—⟫ ⟪—

—⟫ ⟪—

*Freedom isn't the absence of boundaries; it's the ability
to operate successfully and happily within boundaries!*
SHIRLEY BOONE

—⟫ ⟪—

*La Belle Dame Sans Merci,* WALTER CRANE (1845–1915)

# A
# Woman's

*February*

Give, and it will be given to you:
good measure, pressed down,
shaken together, and running over
will be put into your bosom.
For with the same measure that
you use, it will be measured
back to you.

LUKE 6:38

# $\mathcal{F}$EBRUARY

1

2

3

4

5

6

7

NOTES

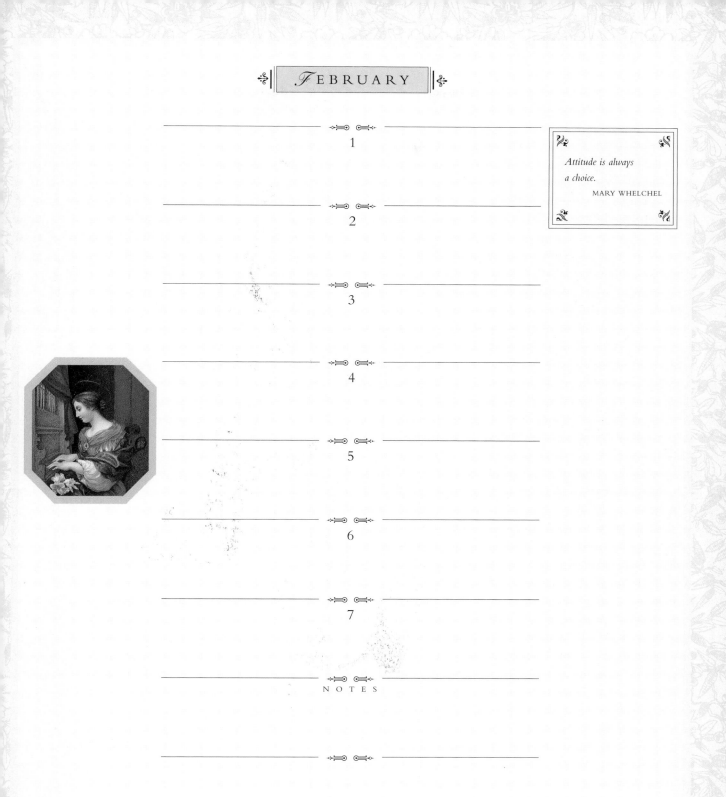

> *Attitude is always a choice.*
> MARY WHELCHEL

LEFT: *Fair Rosamund and Queen Eleanor*, SIR EDWARD COLEY BURNE-JONES (1833–1898)

*Faraway Thoughts,* CHARLES WEST COPE (1811–1890)

# FEBRUARY

8

9

10

11

12

13

14

NOTES

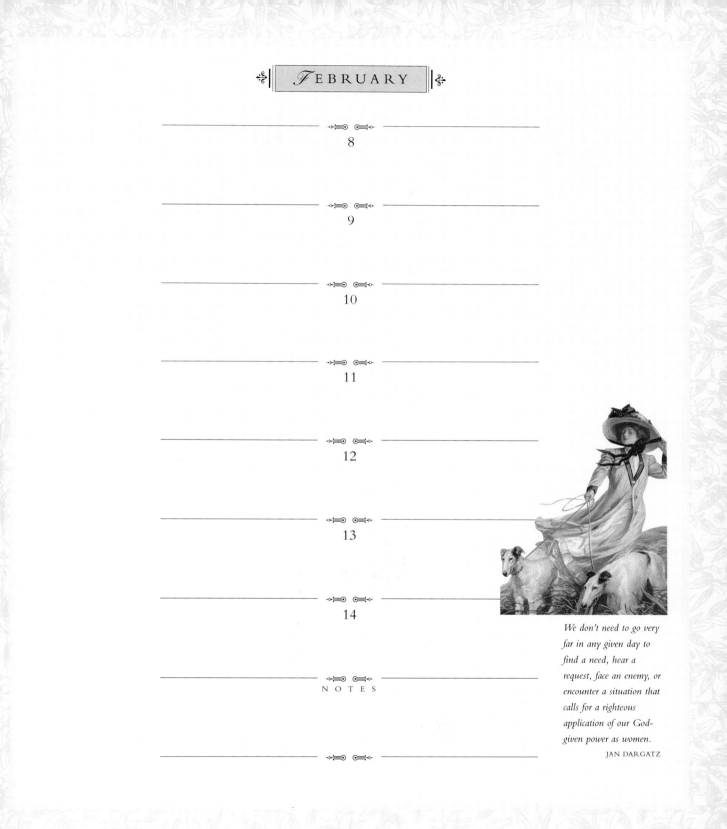

*We don't need to go very far in any given day to find a need, hear a request, face an enemy, or encounter a situation that calls for a righteous application of our God-given power as women.*

JAN DARGATZ

*Flower Arrangement (Teatime)*, SYDNEY MUSCHAMP (fl. 1884–1904)

# FEBRUARY

15

16

17

18

19

20

21

NOTES

*Pleasant words are like
a honeycomb,
Sweetness to the soul
and health to the bones.*

PROVERBS 16:24

———————— 22 ————————

———————— 23 ————————

———————— 24 ————————

———————— 25 ————————

*We can't all leave a prestigious background or lots of money to our children, but we can leave them a legacy of love.*

NAOMI RHODE

———————— 26 ————————

———————— 27 ————————

———————— 28 ————————

———————— 29 ————————

*Fantasia in White*, ALBERT LUDOVICI (1820–1894)

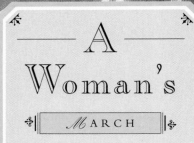

# A Woman's

## MARCH

*Life is not intended to be simply a round of work, no matter how interesting and important that work may be. A moment's pause to watch the glory of a sunrise or a sunset is soul satisfying, while a bird's song will set the steps to music all day long.*

LAURA INGALLS WILDER

# MARCH

1

2

3

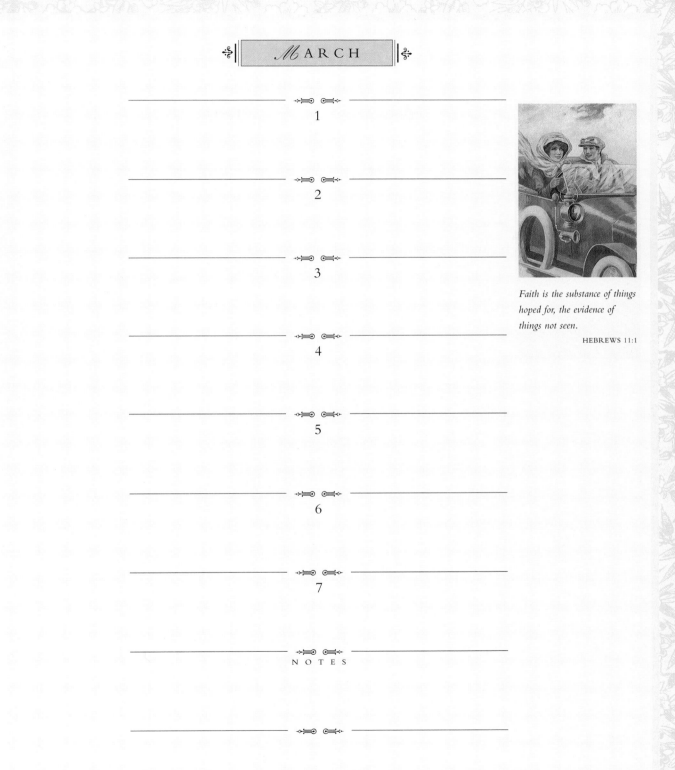

*Faith is the substance of things hoped for, the evidence of things not seen.*

HEBREWS 11:1

4

5

6

7

NOTES

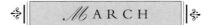 

8

9

10

11

> The history of every
> country begins in the
> heart of a man or
> a woman.
>
> WILLA CATHER

*La Primavera,* detail of
Spring, SANDRO
BOTTICELLI (1445–1510)

*Summer Evening at Skagen, the Artist's Wife
with a Dog on a Beach*
PETER SEVERIN KROYER (1851–1909)

12

13

14

*Real feminism is saying,
"I am who I am. I don't
have to change who I am
to be equal to anyone."*
KAY COLES JAMES

15

16

17

18

> *The eternal way is to hold fast to the simple and profound principles of integrity of the self and respect for others.*
>
> PEARL S. BUCK

19

20

21

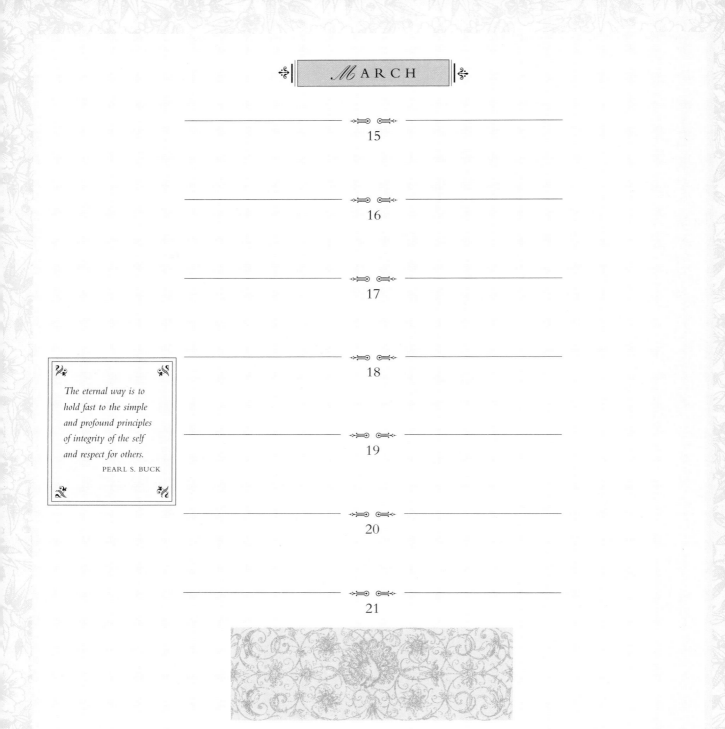

*A Lady of Leisure*, FREDERIC SOULACROIX (1825–1879)

22

23

24

25

26

27

28

*While the spirit of neighborliness was important on the frontier because neighbors were so few, it is even more important now because our neighbors are so many.*

CLAUDIA "LADY BIRD" JOHNSON

NOTES

———— 29 ————

———— 30 ————

———— 31 ————

N O T E S

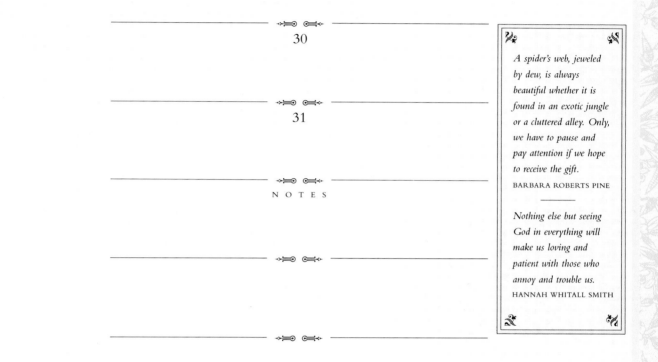

*A spider's web, jeweled by dew, is always beautiful whether it is found in an exotic jungle or a cluttered alley. Only, we have to pause and pay attention if we hope to receive the gift.*

BARBARA ROBERTS PINE

———

*Nothing else but seeing God in everything will make us loving and patient with those who annoy and trouble us.*

HANNAH WHITALL SMITH

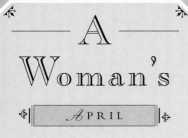

# A Woman's

## APRIL

*No matter how late the hour, no matter how desperate the moment, we cannot despair; the joy and riches God has promised us stretch like a shining road into the future!*

CATHERINE MARSHALL

————————————————— ⟶◉⟵ —————————————————

1

————————————————— ⟶◉⟵ —————————————————

2

————————————————— ⟶◉⟵ —————————————————

3

————————————————— ⟶◉⟵ —————————————————

4

————————————————— ⟶◉⟵ —————————————————

5

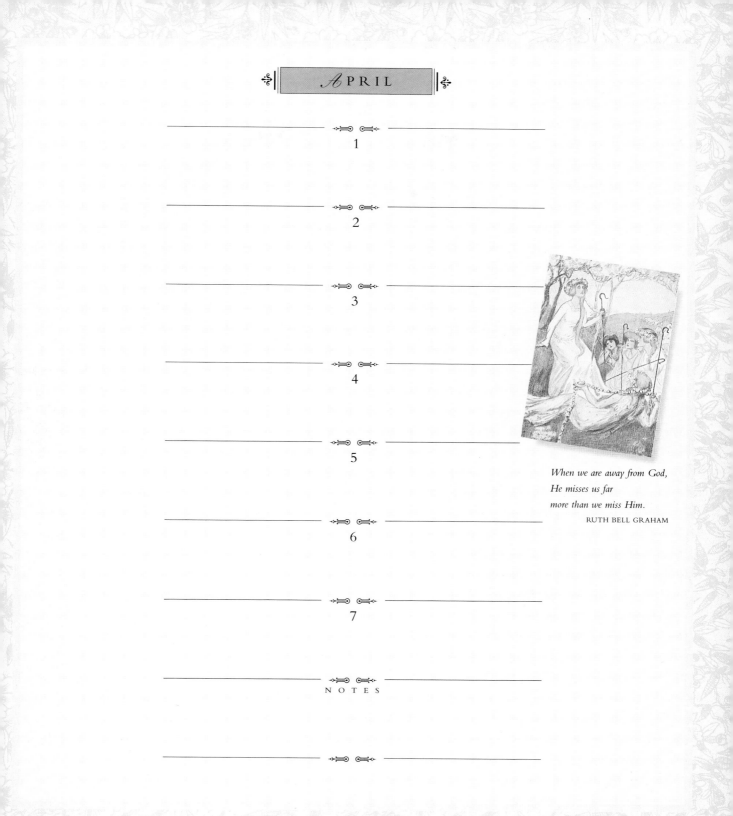

————————————————— ⟶◉⟵ —————————————————

6

*When we are away from God,*
*He misses us far*
*more than we miss Him.*

RUTH BELL GRAHAM

————————————————— ⟶◉⟵ —————————————————

7

————————————————— ⟶◉⟵ —————————————————

NOTES

————————————————— ⟶◉⟵ —————————————————

LEFT: *Going Down Stream*, DAVID WOODLOCK (1842–1929)

*Amaryllis, or The Shepherdess,* WILLIAM HOLMAN HUNT (1827–1910)

8

9

10

11

12

13

14

NOTES

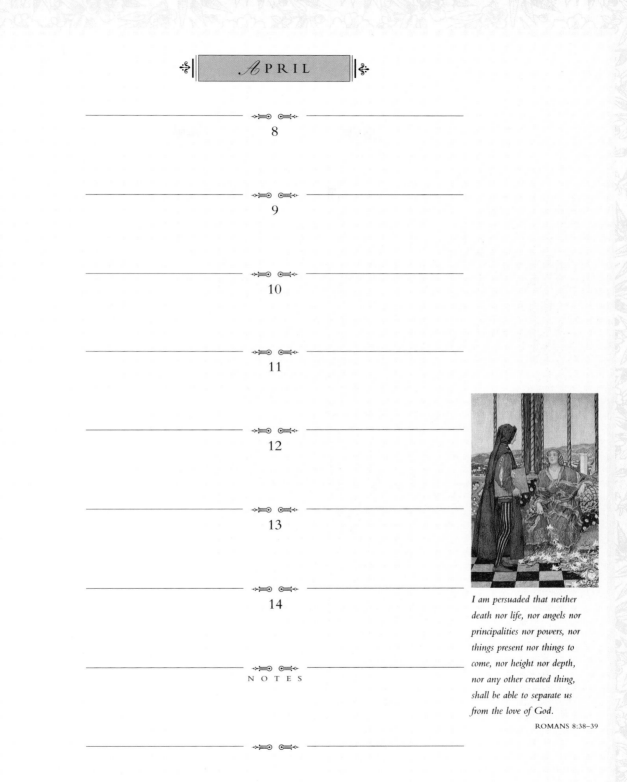

*I am persuaded that neither death nor life, nor angels nor principalities nor powers, nor things present nor things to come, nor height nor depth, nor any other created thing, shall be able to separate us from the love of God.*

ROMANS 8:38–39

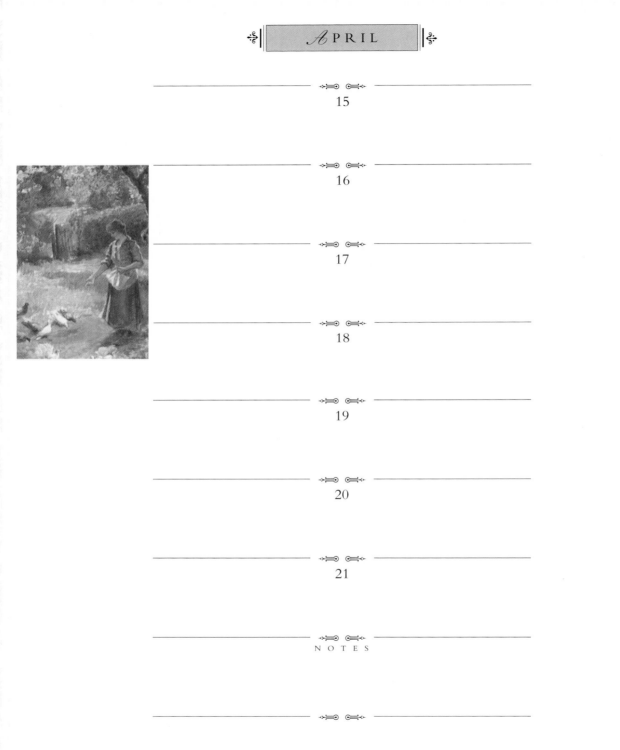

15

16

17

18

19

20

21

NOTES

*A Summer Reverie,* HENRI MARTIN (1860–1943)

---

22

---

23

> If life were predictable it
> would cease to be life and
> be without flavor.
> ELEANOR ROOSEVELT

---

24

---

25

---

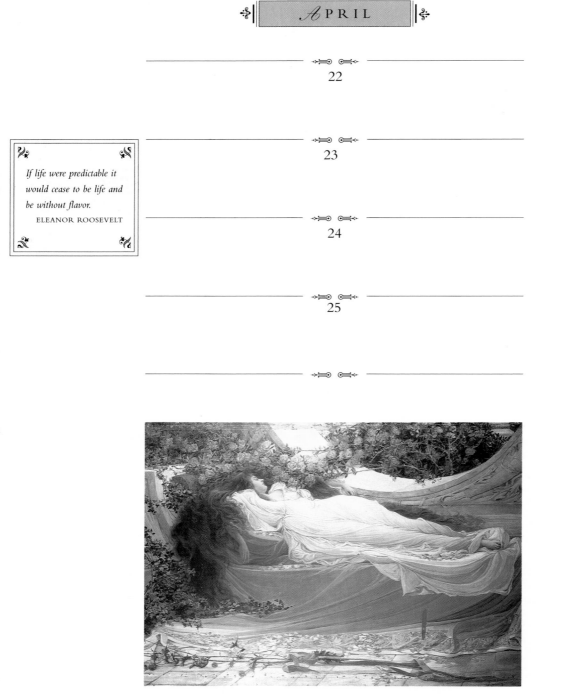

*The Sleeping Beauty,* THOMAS RALPH SPENCE (fl. 1876–1903)

# APRIL

―――――――――――――――― ⬥――⬥ ――――――――――――――――

## 26

―――――――――――――――― ⬥――⬥ ――――――――――――――――

## 27

―――――――――――――――― ⬥――⬥ ――――――――――――――――

## 28

―――――――――――――――― ⬥――⬥ ――――――――――――――――

### NOTES

―――――――――――――――― ⬥――⬥ ――――――――――――――――

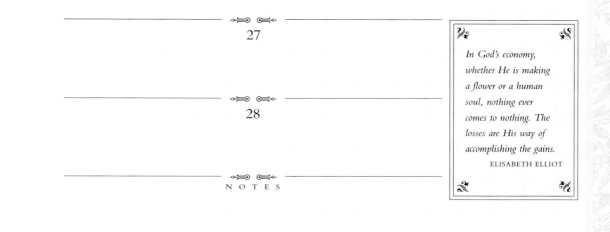

*In God's economy,
whether He is making
a flower or a human
soul, nothing ever
comes to nothing. The
losses are His way of
accomplishing the gains.*
ELISABETH ELLIOT

*Day-Dreams,* JEAN BEAUDUIN (1851–1916)

29

30

NOTES

*Prayer is the pure privilege of
being consciously with God.*

EUGENIA PRICE

*Lilies*, WALTER CRANE (1845–1915)

# A Woman's

### MAY

*"Hope" is the thing with feathers*
*That perches in the soul,*
*And sings the tune*
*without the words,*
*And never stops at all.*
EMILY DICKINSON

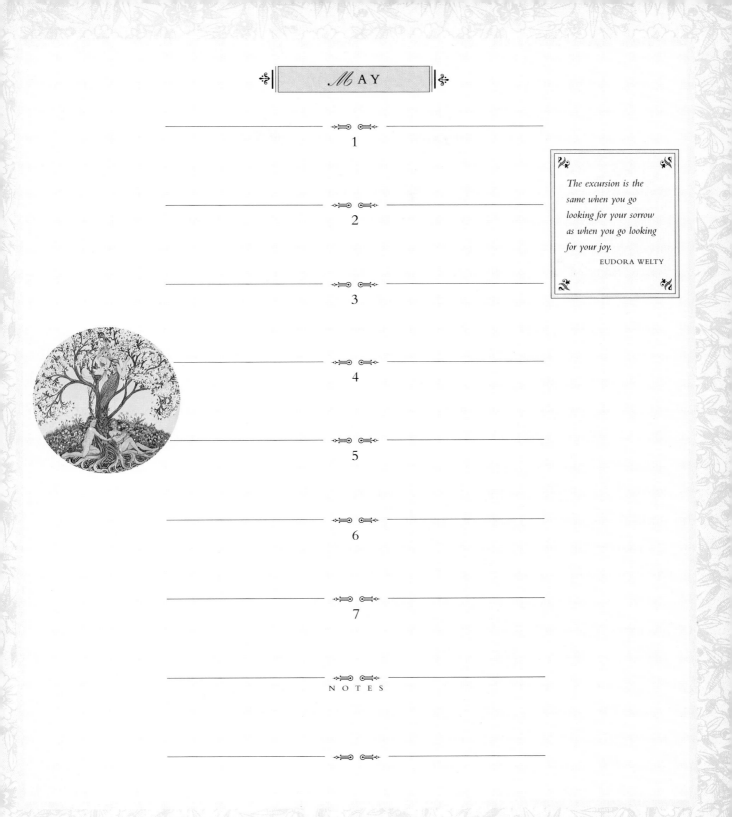

# $\mathcal{M}$ AY

1

2

3

4

5

6

7

*The excursion is the
same when you go
looking for your sorrow
as when you go looking
for your joy.*
EUDORA WELTY

N O T E S

LEFT: *Young Friends,* LEXDEN LEWIS POCOCK (1850–1919)

8

9

10

11

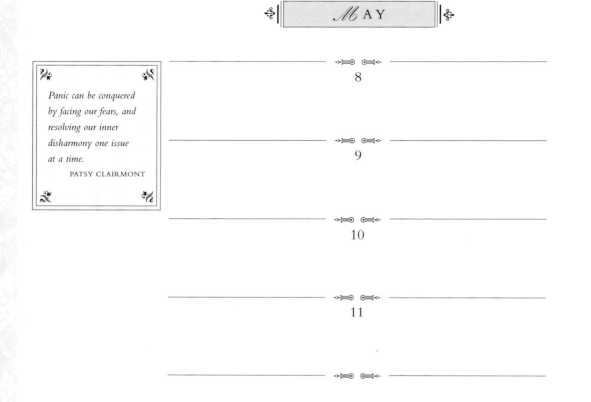

*Panic can be conquered by facing our fears, and resolving our inner disharmony one issue at a time.*

PATSY CLAIRMONT

*Reflections,* WALTER PLIMPTON (fl. 1865–1890)

————— 12 —————

————— 13 —————

————— 14 —————

> *I've learned that when we stop thinking that what we've got is second best and make it the best, our "failure" turns into success.*
>
> SARAH CANNON
> (MINNIE PEARL)

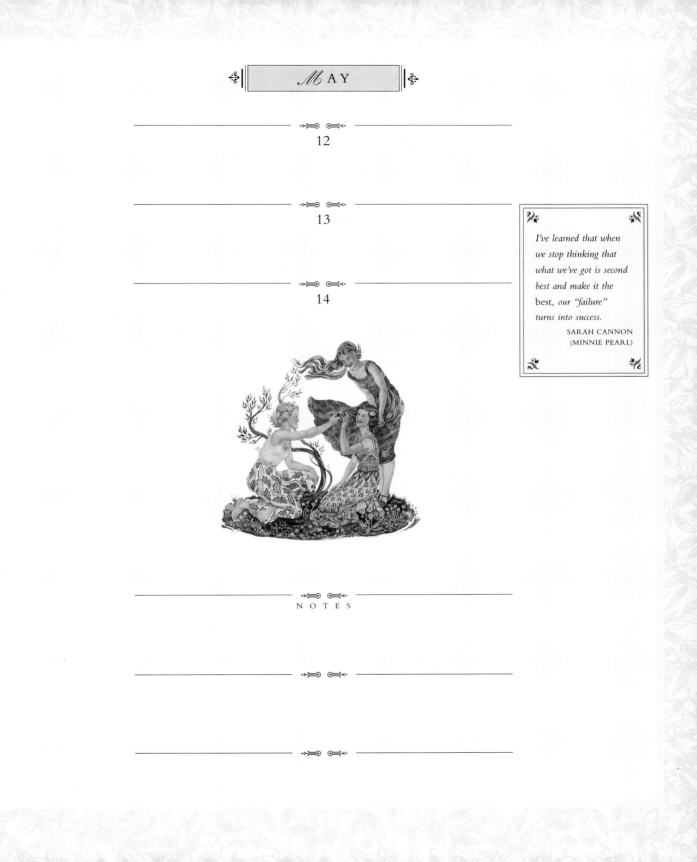

————— N O T E S —————

—————————————— ⇥⊙⇤ ——————————————
15

—————————————— ⇥⊙⇤ ——————————————
16

—————————————— ⇥⊙⇤ ——————————————
17

—————————————— ⇥⊙⇤ ——————————————
18

—————————————— ⇥⊙⇤ ——————————————
19

—————————————— ⇥⊙⇤ ——————————————
20

—————————————— ⇥⊙⇤ ——————————————
21

*Wisdom is more precious than rubies. . . . Her ways are ways of pleasantness, and all her paths are peace.*

EMILIE GRIFFIN

—————————————— ⇥⊙⇤ ——————————————
NOTES

—————————————— ⇥⊙⇤ ——————————————

*A Pensive Mood*, ROGER-JOSEPH JOURDAIN (1845–1918)

Life is like a VCR. If
you're constantly moving
the fast forward, your
days will be a blur. If
you're always reaching
for rewind, you'll miss
some nice surprises.
Instead, enjoy life in the
play mode, content with
each frame that passes
before your eyes.

LIZ CURTIS HIGGS

22

23

24

25

26

27

28

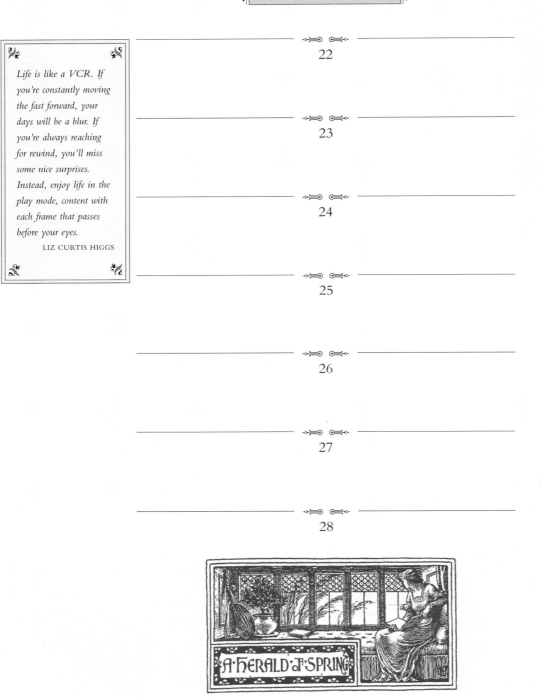

A·HERALD·OF·SPRING

# MAY

---

### 29

---

### 30

---

### 31

---

NOTES

*Change is the true
nature of this world.
Change is the one thing
we can be sure of.*

NAOMI JUDD

---

*Feeding the Ducks,* LOUIS ANTOINE AUGUSTE THOMAS (fl. c. 1865)

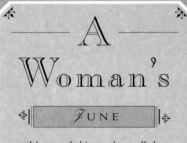

# A
## Woman's

### JUNE

*It's a good thing to have all the
props pulled out from under us
occasionally. It gives us some sense
of what is rock under our feet
and what is sand.*

MADELEINE L'ENGLE

———————— 1 ————————

———————— 2 ————————

———————— 3 ————————

———————— 4 ————————

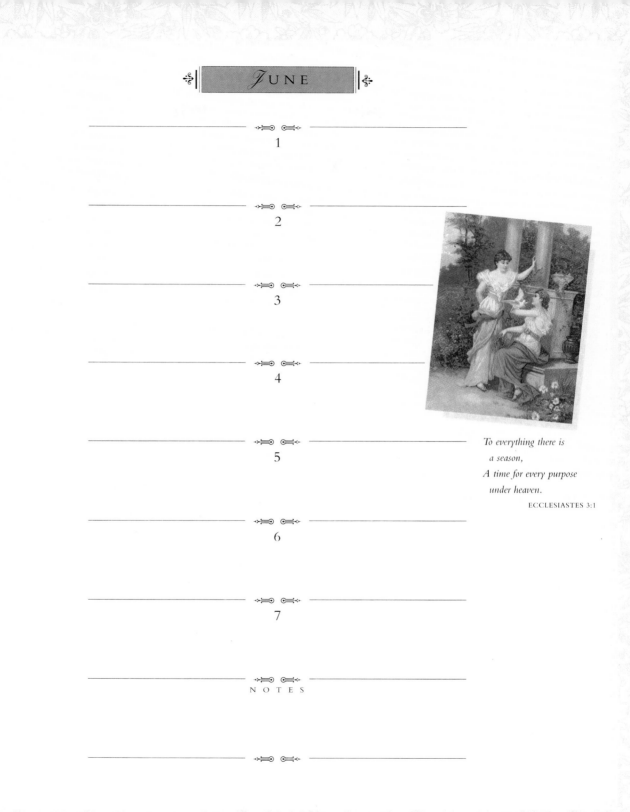

———————— 5 ————————

*To everything there is
a season,
A time for every purpose
under heaven.*

ECCLESIASTES 3:1

———————— 6 ————————

———————— 7 ————————

NOTES

—————————————————

LEFT: *Daydreams*, NORMAN PRESCOTT-DAVIES (1862–1915)

8

9

10

11

12

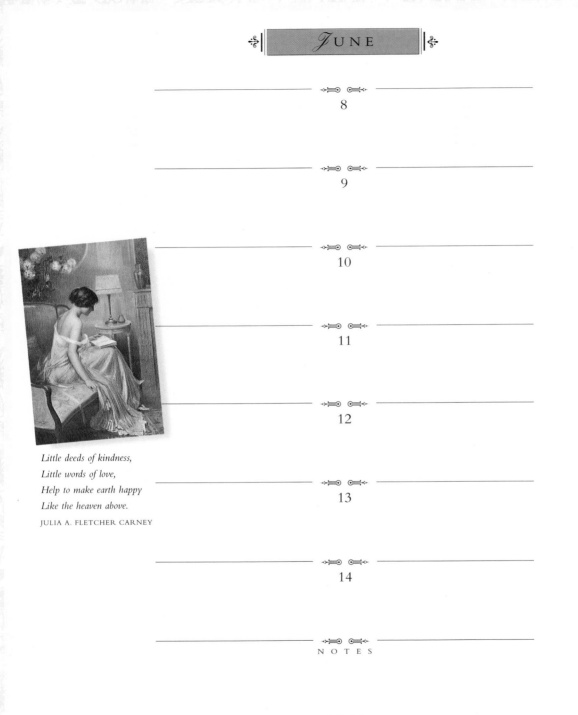

*Little deeds of kindness,*
*Little words of love,*
*Help to make earth happy*
*Like the heaven above.*

JULIA A. FLETCHER CARNEY

13

14

NOTES

*Au Bord de la Mer,* FRANÇOIS FLAMENG (1856–1923)

# JUNE

15

16

17

18

19

20

21

22

*For as the body is clad in the cloth, and the flesh in the skin, and the bones in the flesh, and the heart in the whole, so are we, soul and body, clad in the Goodness of God, and enclosed.*

DAME JULIAN
OF NORWICH

# $\mathscr{J}$UNE

---

23

---

24

---

25

---

26

---

27

---

28

> *Freedom is not the right to do what we want but the power to do what we ought.*
>
> CORRIE TEN BOOM

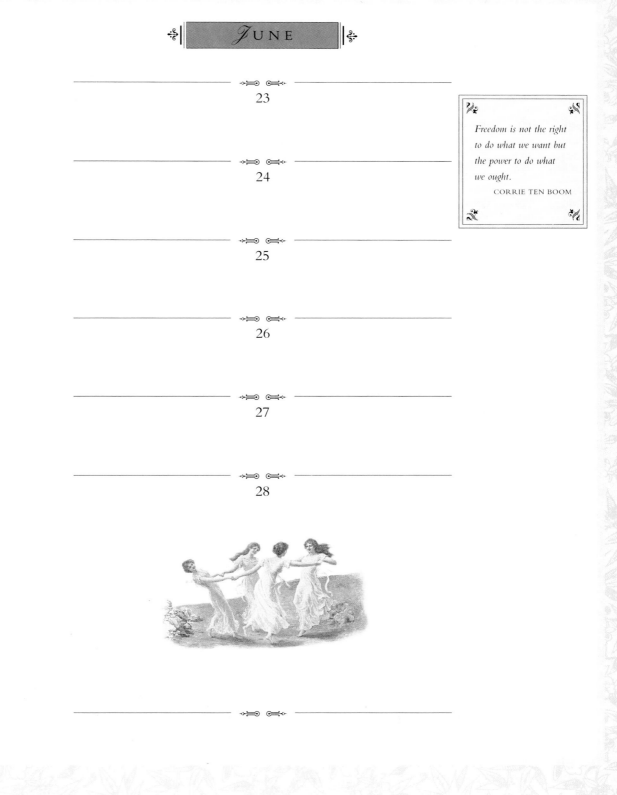

---

*The Flower Maiden*, HENRY JOHN STOCK (1853–1930)

---
### 29

---
### 30

---
### NOTES

---

---

---

> *Vices are simply overworked virtues.*
> LAURA INGALLS WILDER

---

*Faith is what sustains me and my family. It anchors us. Otherwise, we flop around desperately like fish out of water when a crisis comes.*

ANN JILLIAN

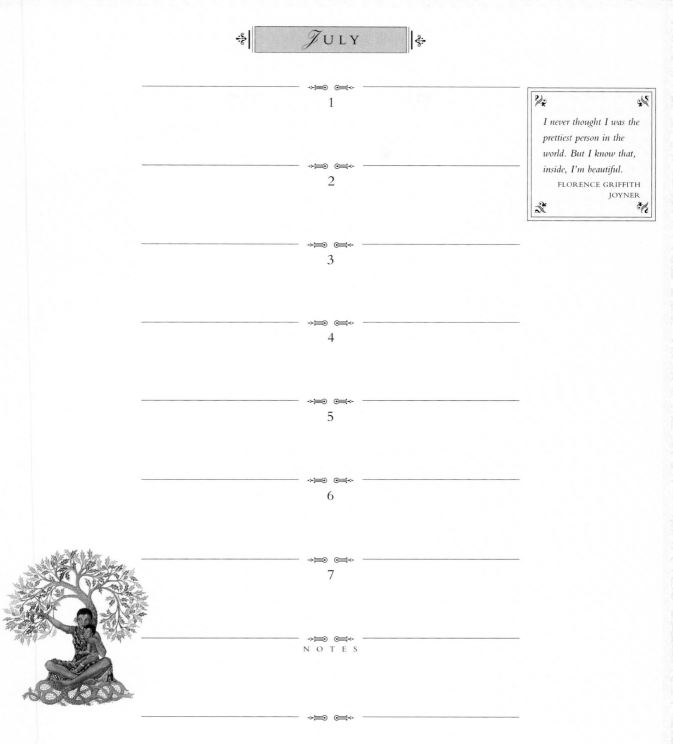

# JULY

1

2

3

4

5

6

7

NOTES

LEFT: *Bathing in the Ganges*, VALENTINE CAMERON PRINSEP (1838–1904)

# JULY

---

8

---

9

---

10

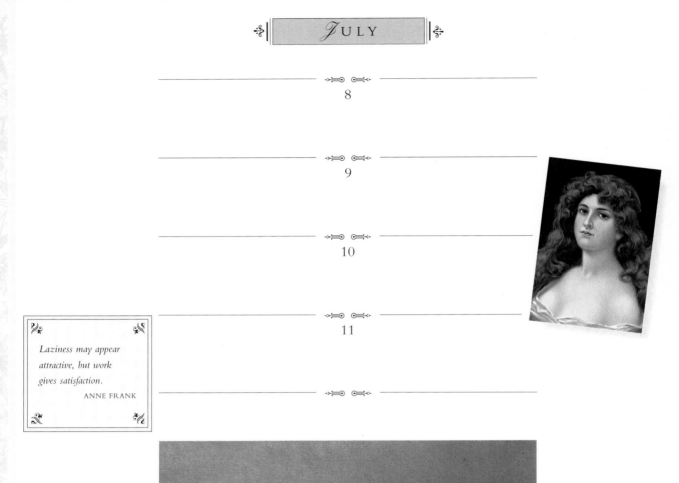

---

11

---

*Summer Evening on the Skagen Southern Beach with Anna Ancher &
Maria Kroyer,* PETER SEVERIN KROYER (1851–1909)

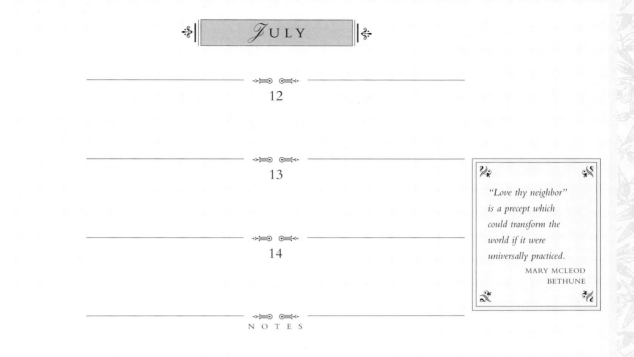

# JULY

───────── 12 ─────────

───────── 13 ─────────

───────── 14 ─────────

───────── NOTES ─────────

───────────────────────

*"Love thy neighbor"
is a precept which
could transform the
world if it were
universally practiced.*

MARY MCLEOD
BETHUNE

*The Letter,* JOHN TOWNSEND (BORN 1929)

# $\mathscr{J}$ULY

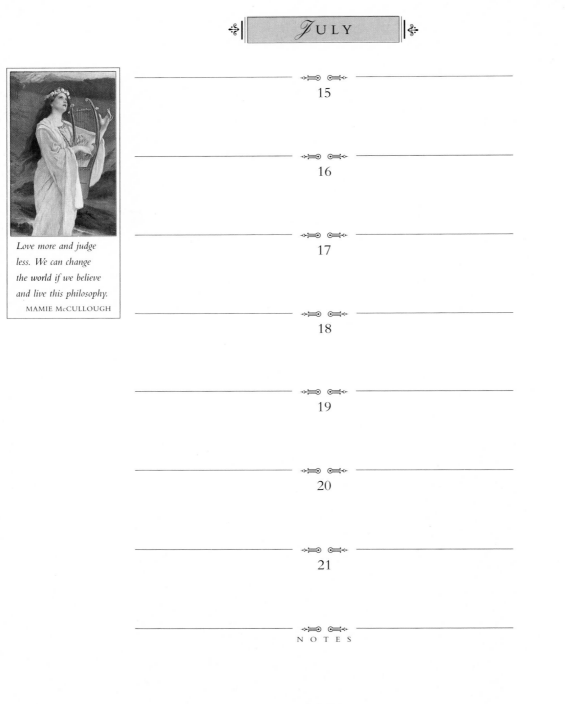

*Love more and judge less. We can change the world if we believe and live this philosophy.*

MAMIE McCULLOUGH

15

16

17

18

19

20

21

NOTES

*The Prelude,* WILLIAM WARDLAW LAING (fl. 1873–1898)

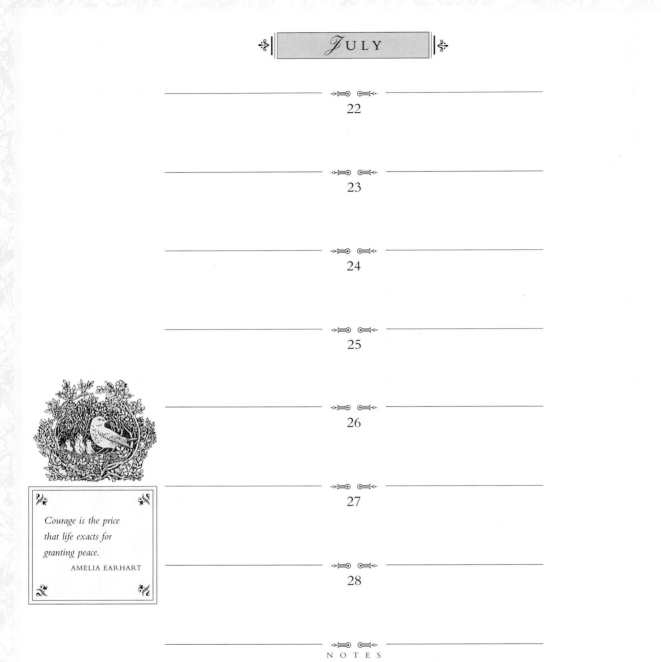

# JULY

22

23

24

25

26

27

*Courage is the price
that life exacts for
granting peace.*

AMELIA EARHART

28

NOTES

---

29

---

30

---

31

---

NOTES

---

> *Faith is like a lily,*
> *lifted high and white.*
> CHRISTINA ROSSETTI

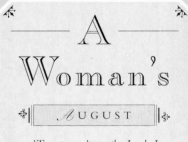

*'Twant me, 'twas the Lord. I always told him, "I trust you. I don't know where to go or what to do, but I expect you to lead me," and he always did.*

HARRIET TUBMAN

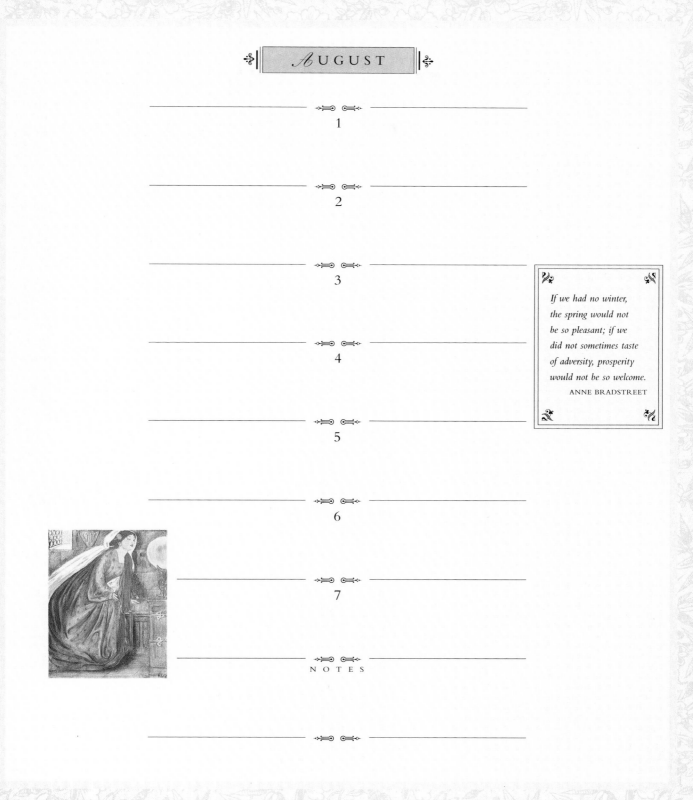

# $\mathcal{A}$UGUST

1

2

3

4

5

6

7

NOTES

*If we had no winter,
the spring would not
be so pleasant; if we
did not sometimes taste
of adversity, prosperity
would not be so welcome.*
ANNE BRADSTREET

LEFT: *Innocent Youth,* TOM MOSTYN (1864–1930)

# $\mathscr{A}$UGUST

8

9

10

11

12

13

14

NOTES

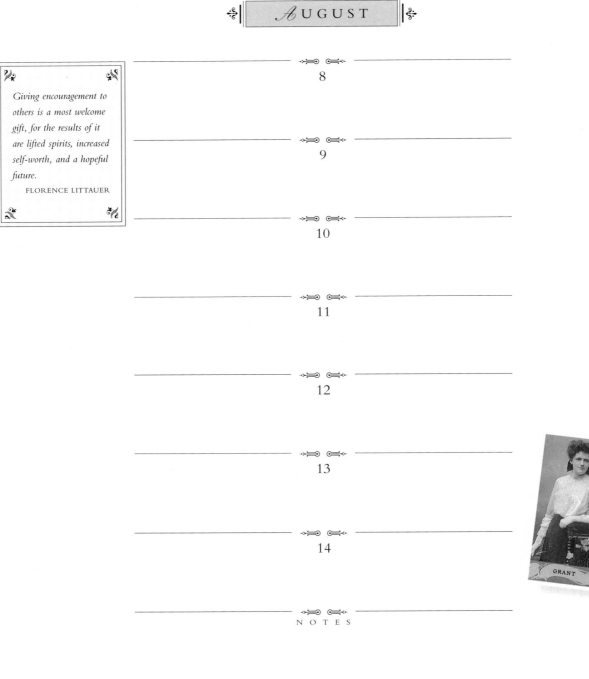

GRANT

*The Sweet Smell of the Rose*, ARTHUR GREENBANK (fl. 1880–1900)

*Love's Spell*, GEORGE FREDERICK CHESTER (fl. 1861–1889)

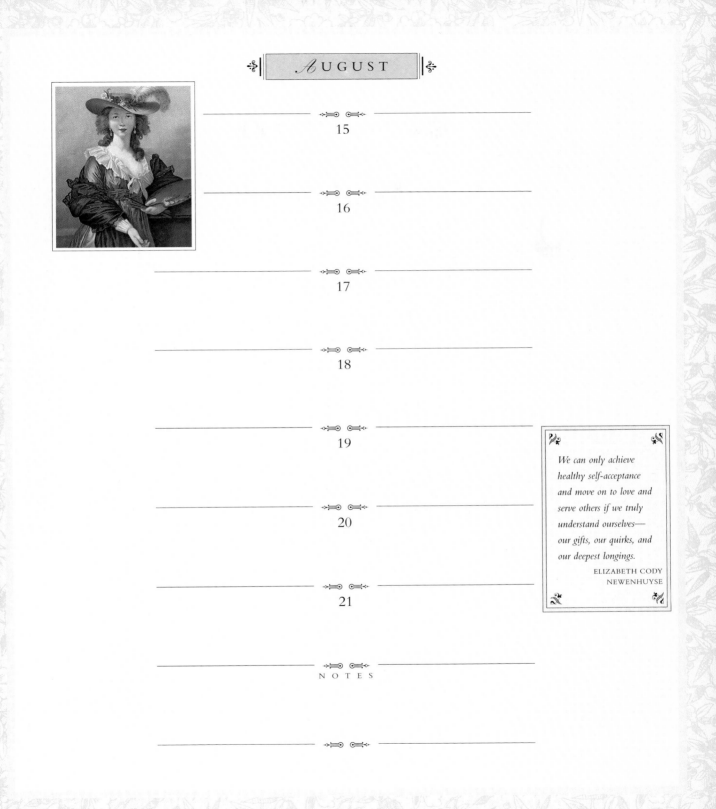

15

16

17

18

19

20

21

NOTES

*We can only achieve
healthy self-acceptance
and move on to love and
serve others if we truly
understand ourselves—
our gifts, our quirks, and
our deepest longings.*

ELIZABETH CODY
NEWENHUYSE

22

23

*We never know how*
*high we are*
*Till we are called to rise;*
*And then, if we are true*
*to plan,*
*Our statures touch*
*the skies.*

EMILY DICKINSON

24

25

26

27

28

NOTES

*The Kiosk*, FRANCIS JOHN WYBURD (fl. 1846–1893)

_____ 29

_____ 30

_____ 31

NOTES

*It's not a disgrace to fail,*
*but it's a sin to do less*
*than your best.*

BARBARA JOHNSON

*Comparing Cards*, ANONYMOUS (19/20TH CENTURY)

# A
# Woman's

*Like billowing clouds, like the
incessant gurgle of the brook,
the longing of the soul can never
be stilled. It is this longing with
which holy persons seek their
work from God.*

HILDEGARD OF BINGEN

# $\mathcal{S}$EPTEMBER

1

2

3

4

5

6

7

NOTES

> *Goals are access lines to the future. They allow us to run the race with the finish line firmly established.*
>
> EMILIE BARNES

LEFT: *Le Rendez-vouz*, HARRY JOHN PEARSON (1872–1933)

8

9

10

11

> *God allows us to have places of darkness so we can appreciate the light more.*
>
> LUCI SHAW

*Letter, with Quill Pen,* ADOLPHE PIOT (c. 1890)

# *S*EPTEMBER

THE ANNUNCIATION, EDWARD REGINALD FRAMPTON (1872–1923)

*I believe laughter is like a needle and thread. Deftly used, it can patch up just about everything.*
BARBARA JOHNSON

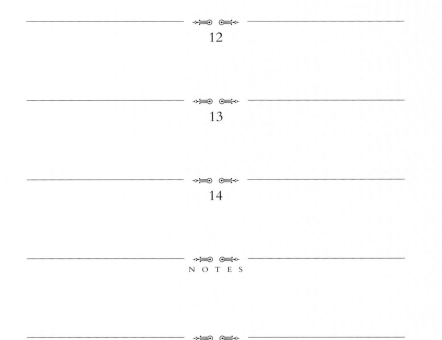

---

12

---

13

---

14

---

NOTES

---

# SEPTEMBER

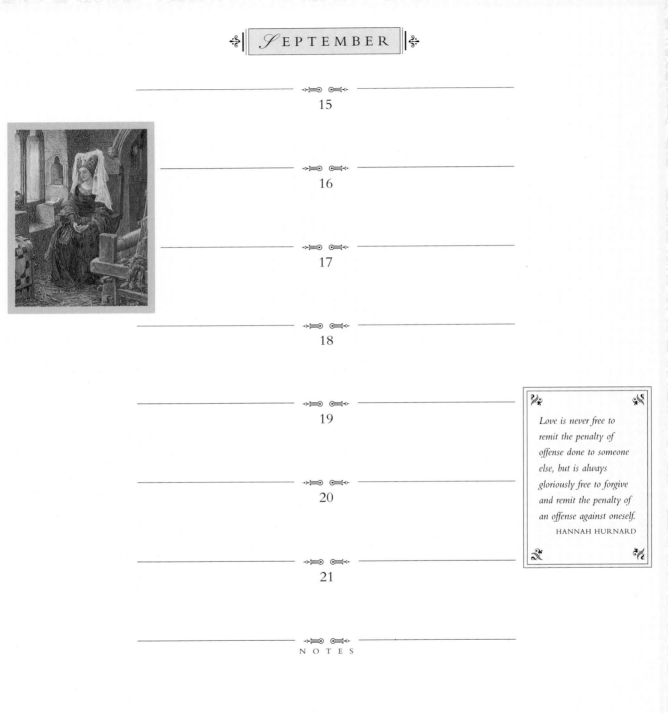

15

16

17

18

19

20

21

NOTES

*Love is never free to remit the penalty of offense done to someone else, but is always gloriously free to forgive and remit the penalty of an offense against oneself.*
HANNAH HURNARD

*La Primavera*, detail of three graces, SANDRO BOTTICELLI (1445–1510)

# $\mathscr{S}$EPTEMBER

22

23

*How careful we should be with our words, when we consider the lasting power for good or evil of one hastily spoken sentence.*

FLORENCE LITTAUER

24

25

26

27

28

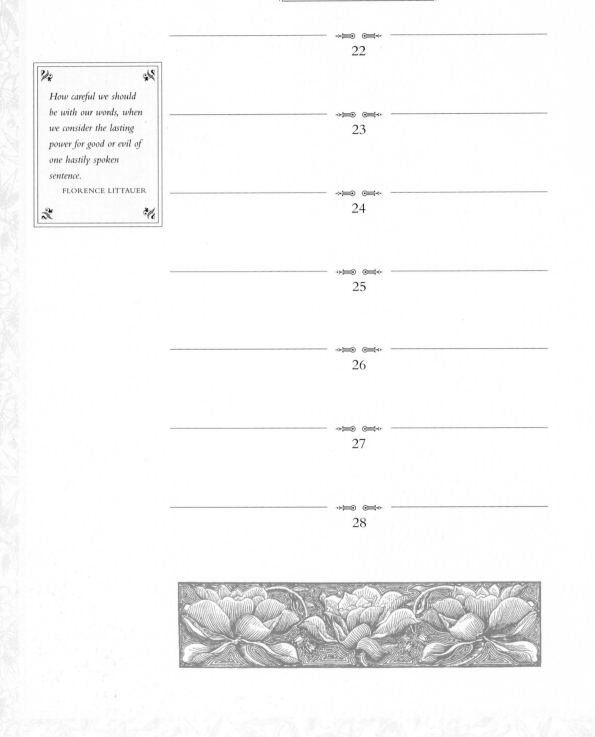

# $\mathscr{S}$EPTEMBER

---

29

---

30

---

NOTES

---

---

---

---

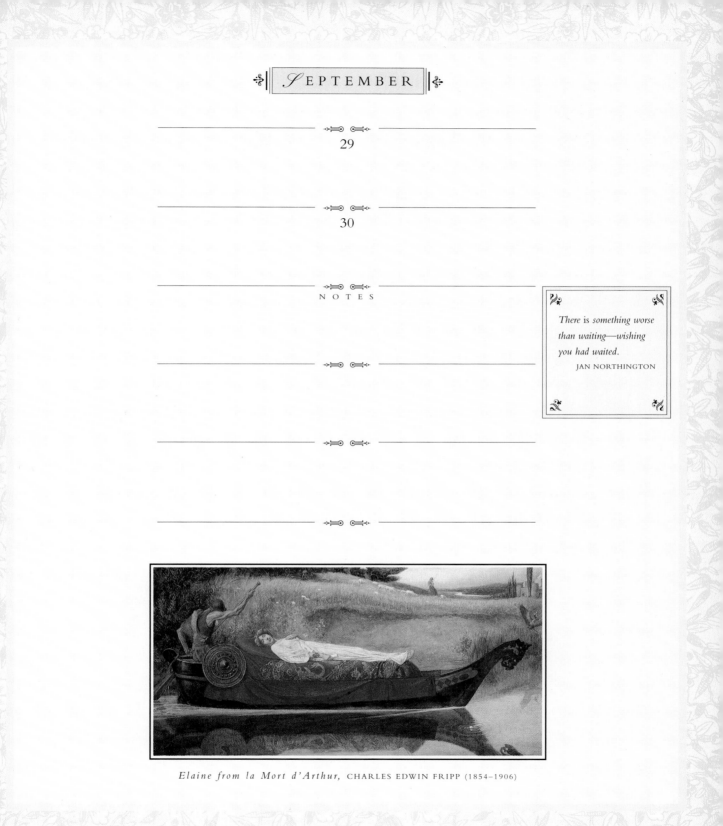

*Elaine from la Mort d'Arthur,* CHARLES EDWIN FRIPP (1854–1906)

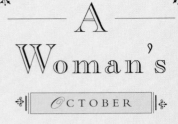

# A Woman's

### October

*Whatever things are true, whatever
things are noble, whatever things
are just, whatever things are pure,
whatever things are lovely,
whatever things are of good report,
if there is any virtue and if there
is anything praiseworthy
—meditate on these things.*

PHILIPPIANS 4:8

Holyoake

# $\mathscr{O}$CTOBER

1

2

3

4

5

6

7

NOTES

*Spread love everywhere you go: first of all in your own home. Give love to your children, to your wife or husband, to a next-door neighbor.*

MOTHER TERESA

# OCTOBER

8

9

10

11

*The soul of a righteous person is nothing but a paradise, in which, as God tells us, he takes his delight.*

ST. TERESA OF AVILA

12

13

14

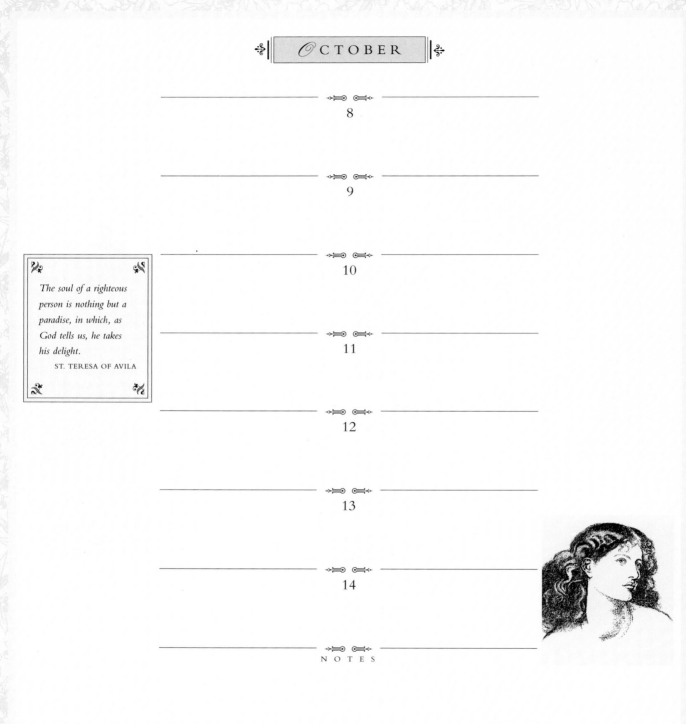

NOTES

*Carrying the Peacock*, JOHN DAWSON WATSON (1832–1892)

# OCTOBER

———— 15 ————

———— 16 ————

> *Lord, I do fear*
> *Thou'st made the world*
> *too beautiful this year.*
> EDNA ST. VINCENT MILLAY

———— 17 ————

———— 18 ————

———— 19 ————

———— 20 ————

———— 21 ————

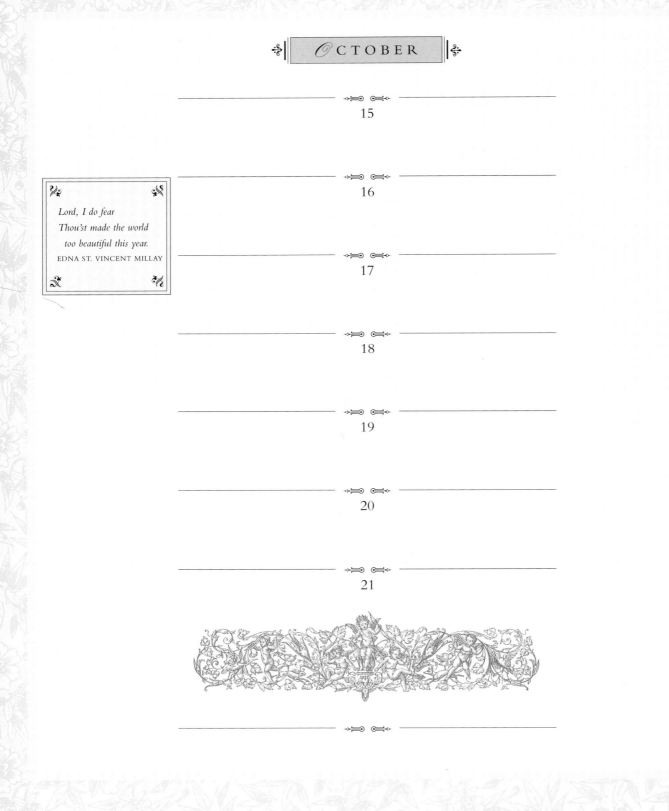

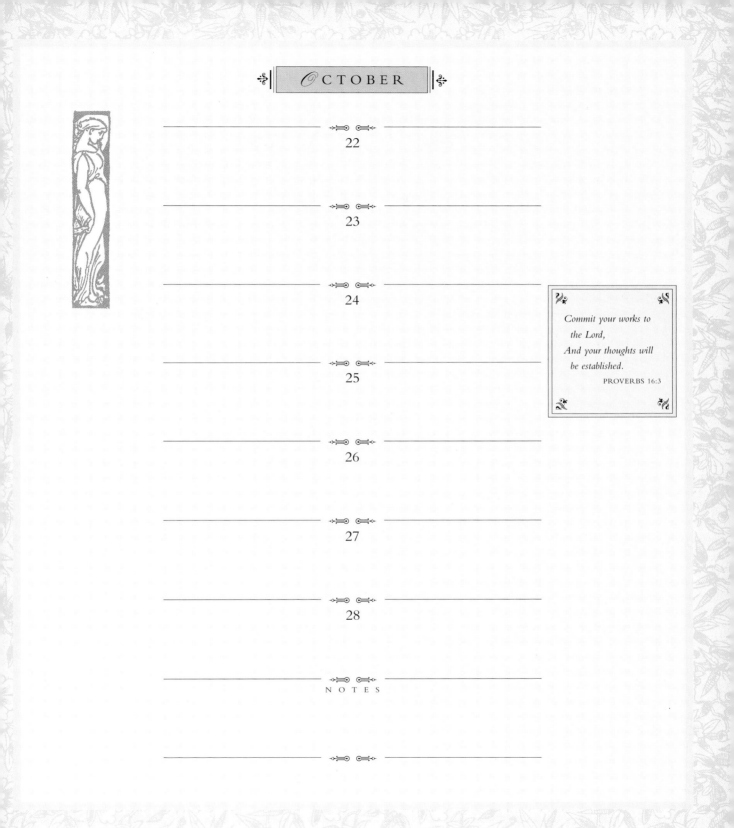

# OCTOBER

22

23

24

*Commit your works to
the Lord,
And your thoughts will
be established.*

PROVERBS 16:3

25

26

27

28

NOTES

*When Sorrow Comes in Summer Days, Roses Bloom in Vain*
JOHN MELHUISH STRUDWICK (1849–1937)

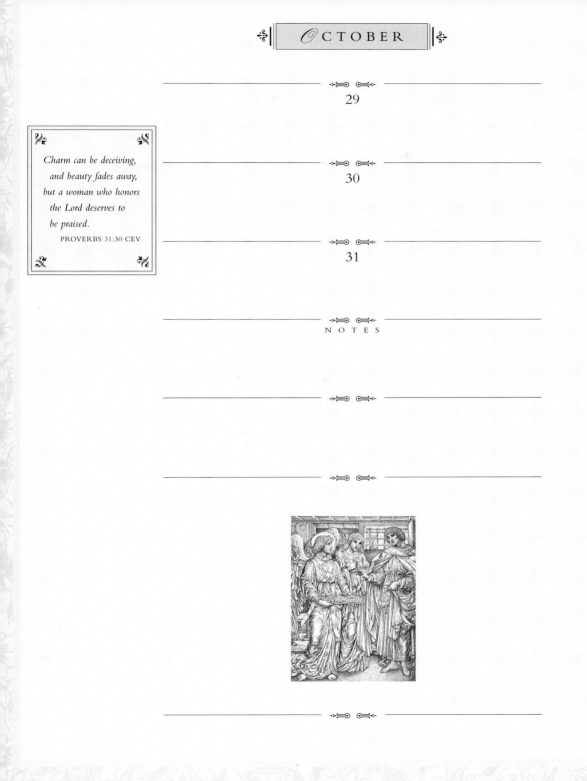

# OCTOBER

---
29

---
30

*Charm can be deceiving,*
*and beauty fades away,*
*but a woman who honors*
*the Lord deserves to*
*be praised.*

PROVERBS 31:30 CEV

---
31

---
NOTES

---

---

---

# A Woman's

*My precious family and friends
have taught me that joy and
sorrow, storms and sunshine,
tears and laughter are all part of
living—and the sun does shine
on the other side.*

MARGARET JENSEN

# NOVEMBER

1

2

3

Even the sour notes of
life . . . are not without
purpose and are never
completely immune to
redemption, grace, and a
certain magic.

DEFORIA LANE

4

5

6

7

NOTES

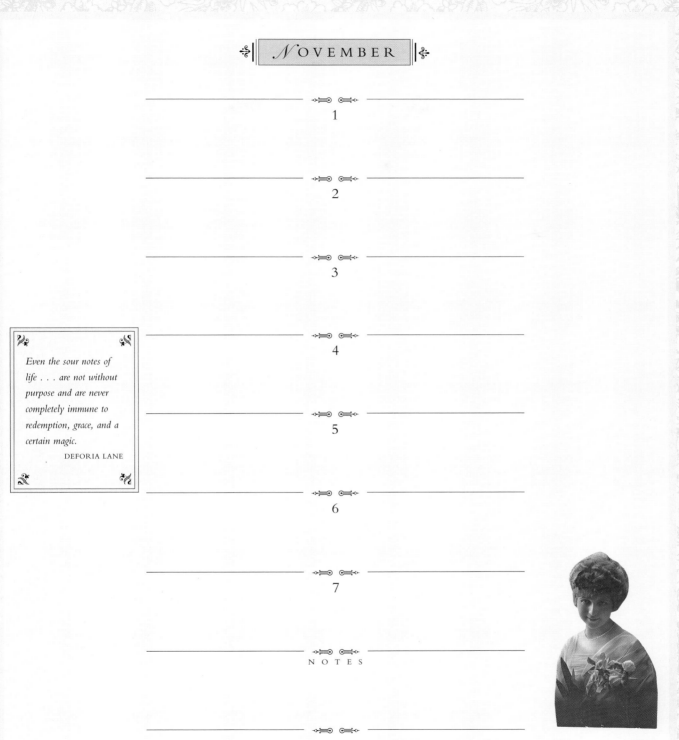

8

9

> *Hard work can make up*
> *for a lack of talent. Work*
> *with what you have . . .*
> *Give 100 percent in*
> *whatever you do.*
>
> MARY JOE FERNANDEZ

10

11

12

13

14

NOTES

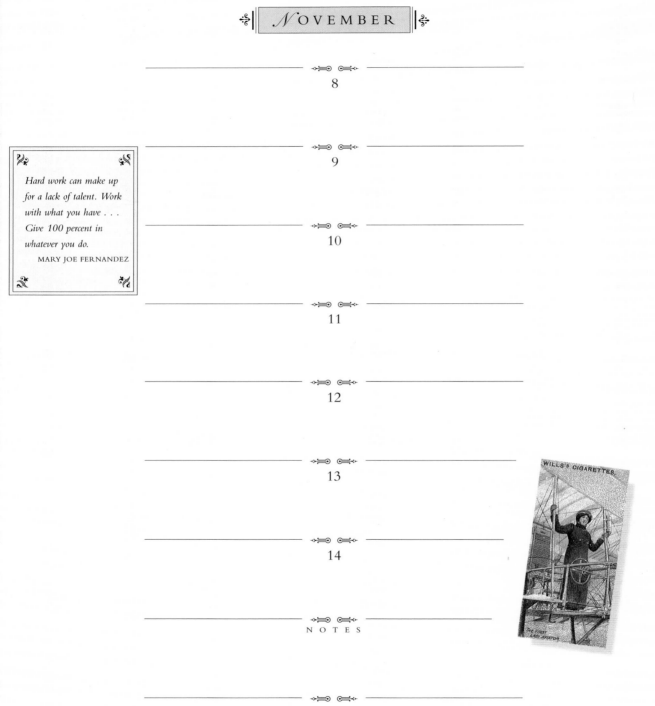

WILLS'S CIGARETTES.

THE FIRST
LADY AVIATOR

15

16

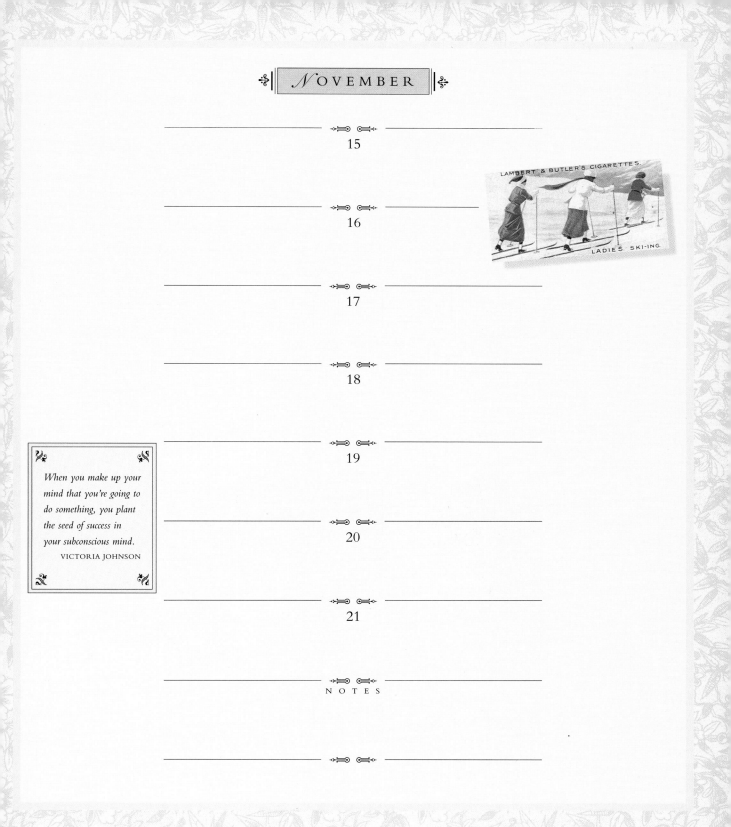

LAMBERT & BUTLER'S CIGARETTES.

LADIES SKI-ING.

17

18

19

*When you make up your mind that you're going to do something, you plant the seed of success in your subconscious mind.*

VICTORIA JOHNSON

20

21

NOTES

―――――――――――――――― ⊶◉◉⊷ ――――――――――――――――
22

―――――――――――――――― ⊶◉◉⊷ ――――――――――――――――
23

―――――――――――――――― ⊶◉◉⊷ ――――――――――――――――
24

―――――――――――――――― ⊶◉◉⊷ ――――――――――――――――
25

―――――――――――――――― ⊶◉◉⊷ ――――――――――――――――

*No past*
*is dead for us,*
*but only*
*sleeping, Love.*

HELEN HUNT JACKSON

*At the Theatre*, JAMES HAYLLAR (1829–1920)

———— 26 ————

———— 27 ————

———— 28 ————

———— NOTES ————

> *The biggest handicap in the world is negative thinking.*
> HEATHER WHITESTONE

————

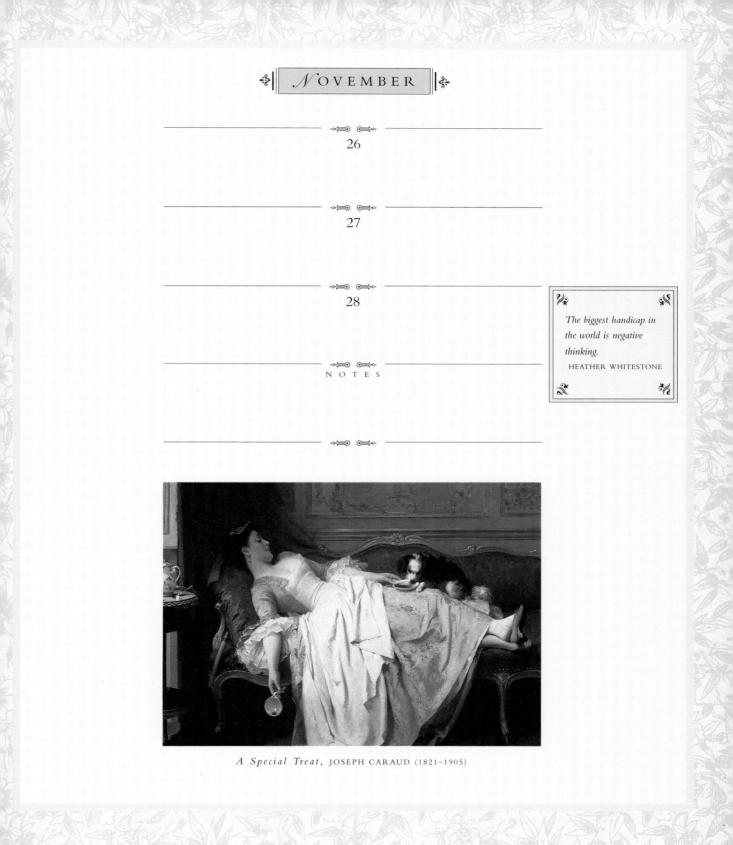

*A Special Treat,* JOSEPH CARAUD (1821–1905)

———————————— 29 ————————————

———————————— 30 ————————————

*Good humor enhances health and
lightens the burdens of life.*
GRACE KETTERMAN

———————————— N O T E S ————————————

*Romantic Thoughts*, WALTER ANDERSON (fl. 1856–1886)

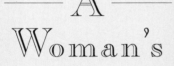

# A Woman's

*I have finally come to understand
that it is only in the silence that I
can hear the story of my life and
the voice of God talking to me
through the telling of it.*

PEGGY BENSON

# DECEMBER

--- ⟶⟿ ---
### 1

--- ⟶⟿ ---
### 2

--- ⟶⟿ ---
### 3

--- ⟶⟿ ---
### 4

--- ⟶⟿ ---
### 5

--- ⟶⟿ ---
### 6

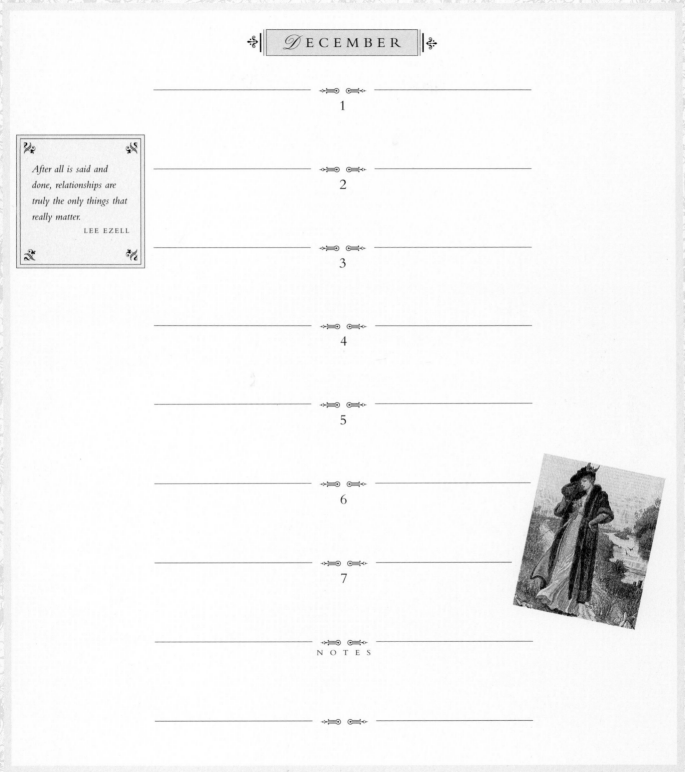

--- ⟶⟿ ---
### 7

--- ⟶⟿ ---
NOTES

--- ⟶⟿ ---

LEFT: *A Favourite Piece*, RAIMONDO DE MADRAZO (1841–1920)

# DECEMBER

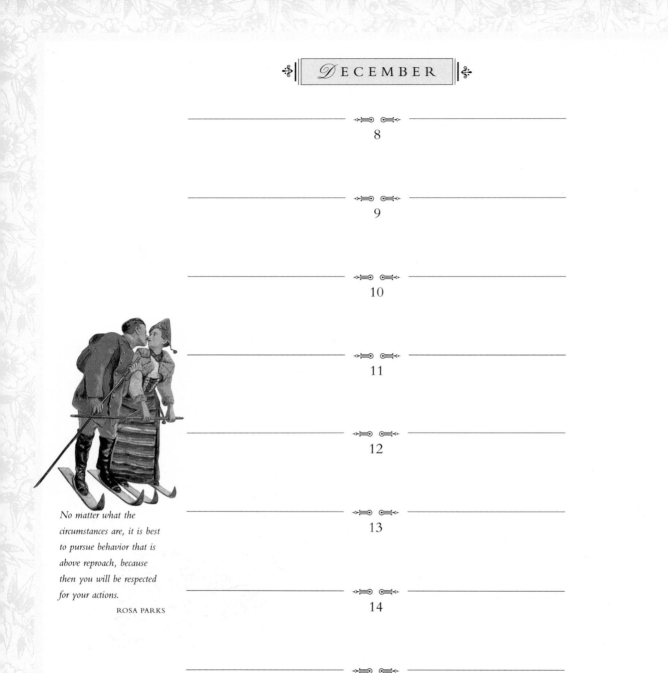

8

9

10

11

12

13

14

*No matter what the
circumstances are, it is best
to pursue behavior that is
above reproach, because
then you will be respected
for your actions.*

ROSA PARKS

NOTES

*In the Park*, GEORGE DUNLOP LESLIE (1835–1921)

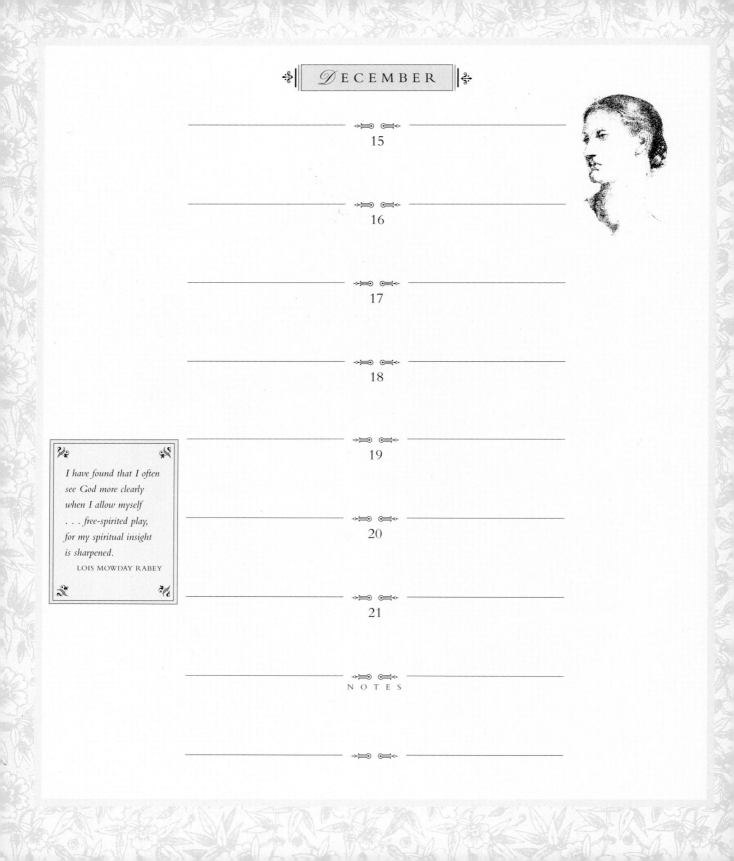

15

16

17

18

19

*I have found that I often
see God more clearly
when I allow myself
. . . free-spirited play,
for my spiritual insight
is sharpened.*

LOIS MOWDAY RABEY

20

21

NOTES

# DECEMBER

22

23

24

25

26

*Learning to say no to
what is not a top priority
and yes only to the
requests that fit into
my personal mission
statement . . . has been
one of the best skills I
have learned.*

BECKY TIRABASSI

27

28

NOTES

# $\mathscr{D}$ECEMBER

---

29

---

30

---

31

---

NOTES

---

> *Don't cry over things
> that were or things that
> aren't. Enjoy what you
> have now to the fullest.*
>
> BARBARA BUSH

---

---

---

---

*A Symphony*, JOHN MELHUISH STRUDWICK (1849–1937)